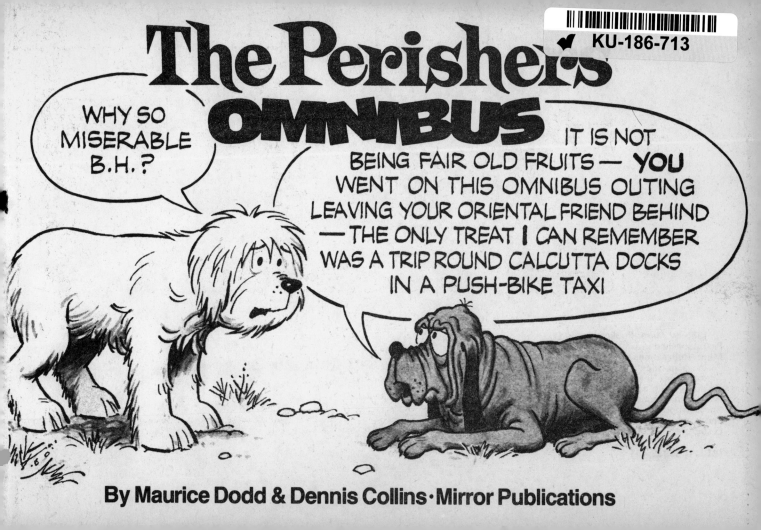

The Perishers OMNIBUS

WHY SO MISERABLE B.H. ?

IT IS NOT BEING FAIR OLD FRUITS — **YOU** WENT ON THIS OMNIBUS OUTING LEAVING YOUR ORIENTAL FRIEND BEHIND — THE ONLY TREAT **I** CAN REMEMBER WAS A TRIP ROUND CALCUTTA DOCKS IN A PUSH-BIKE TAXI

By Maurice Dodd & Dennis Collins · Mirror Publications

© 1985 by Mirror Publications Ltd.
First published in Great Britain in 1985 by
Mirror Publications Ltd., Maxwell House,
74 Worship Street, London EC2A 2EN for
Mirror Group Newspapers Ltd.
Colour printing by The Friary Press, Dorchester.
Printed and bound in Great Britain by
Spottiswoode Ballantyne Ltd., Colchester
and London. Distributed by Argus Press Sales &
Distribution Ltd., London

ISBN 0 85939 491 3

1. Hold tight, please.

Welcome aboard this omnibus in which every page is double-decked with smiles. Occasionally you may be moved to laughter, so be careful as to where you are before glancing between these covers. There are times and places where being moved to laughter can get you moved to one of several institutions, and it won't be any use blaming us—we're not insured for it.

For those unfamiliar with the cartoon strip these few pages are intended to introduce the main characters. They are also intended to give some clue as to what's going on. An act of supreme optimism, as it happens, since even the creators don't know that.

A glance at your top left. Wait. For the benefit of readers now trying to squint up at their receding hairlines, I'll rephrase that. A glance at the top left corner *of this page* will show two of the leading characters getting things off to a swinging start. The four-legged one, conducting an interesting experiment in the aerodynamic capabilities of small boys, is called Boot. He's an Old English Sheepdog (of sorts) who believes himself to be not a dog at all but an eighteenth-century aristocrat, encorcelled into his hirsute husk by the potent curse of a Gipsy wench.

The airborne boy is Wellington so named after his own footwear. He is a noted man of letters—mostly begging letters—an activity necessitated by having to make a living for himself and a large unemployed hairy dog. It's a hard life and things sometimes get a bit desperate. Just how desperate you can judge by a glance at the vignette, to the right, where Wellington is trying to persuade Boot to purchase a low-mileage, one-previous-owner broom.

2. Pass along the bus.

As you pass along the bus you will come across Marlon—and Maisie. No matter how often Marlon may change seats, Maisie will follow.

Maisie has a consuming passion for Marlon, but she would be hard put to explain why. Maybe it's his wild untamed hair, equalled only by his wild untamed toes. Maybe it's the vacant smile which embellishes his air of utter idiocy. Maybe it's the unusual location of his brain (which is in his boots) or maybe it's just because she finds him to be a perfect place on which to rest her weary feet, as shown top left. Whatever it is, Maisie can't put her finger on it—mostly because Marlon moves rapidly from the scene whenever Maisie extends a digit—or anything else—in his direction.

Marlon doesn't reciprocate Maisie's passion (come to that, Marlon doesn't reciprocate anything—it's a manoeuvre too complicated for his capabilities) even though she'd cling to him through thick and thin—or in his case thick and thick—an action she's shown performing in the lower right-hand corner. It could be because Maisie displays the charm of a sackful of old army boots and the temperament of a wasp with earache, although you'd have thought Marlon would at least find novelty value in a girl whose voice brings woodworm screaming out of the woodwork and the directors of Rentokil out in protest at unfair competition. Marlon, though, believes that associating with girls saps a bloke's vitality. This is because he had an uncle who drank two bottles of rum a day and then ran about kissing women and, as Marlon not unreasonably points out, it killed him.

3. Hold tighter, pass along further and oh, cripes, what's happened to the driver?

Passing further along the bus you may find Baby Grumpling, probably under a seat, but more likely on top of or under the bus. If the bus is stationary—having broken down— then it's a safe bet Baby Grumpling has somehow brought about its immobile state. An upward glance to your left will reveal he has a certain mechanical bent.

Anybody wishing to find Baby Grumpling had better start by looking in places a baby shouldn't be and then continue to places a baby *couldn't* be and, if that doesn't make sense, well, anybody who had any sense wouldn't go looking for Baby Grumpling in the first place.

In fact, if you wait long enough Baby Grumpling will find you. If you find your sojourn at the loo longer than you'd planned, owing to a liberal and unexpected application of glue to the seat, you can sit and surmise that Grumpling has passed that way. If, at some jolly function, you find yourself clutching an unsolicited worm sandwich and glimpse Grumpling's shadow flitting for the exit, you'll know his blithe spirit has just contributed something to liven up your mundane life. And next time you find a spider in the bath, you'll know the rotten little kid has been at it again.

There must *be* a solution to Baby Grumpling. Maisie thought she'd found it in the hopeful scene shown lower right, but somebody, not in full possession of the facts, dug him up again.

Just one more thing. If you're considering getting off this omnibus, you've left it too late. This vehicle is now out of control.

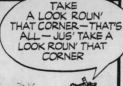

R.44

R.45

R.124

R.125

D'YOU KNOW WHAT I'VE DECIDED TO BE WHEN I GROW UP, BOOT?

— A CREATIVE GENIUS

R296

Maurice Dodd

OH, SO AMBITION HAS GOT TO YOU AT LAST, HAS IT?

HITHERTO YOU'VE BEEN CONTENT TO BE MERELY A COWBOY GENIUS, AND A PIRATE GENIUS, AND A SPACE-MAN GENIUS AND...

I'D BETTER START OFF THE CREATIVE GENIUS LARK BY THINKIN' SOME REALLY HIGH-POWERED-SUPER-T'RIFFIC CREATIVE THOUGHTS

R297

COR

CRUMBS

PHEW

SIGH

IT'S NOT EASY-I CAN TELL YOU, BOOT

WELL AT LEAST IT'S BECOME CLEAR WHAT MY FIRST COURSE OF ACTION'S GOTTA BE...

—ATTENDIN' TO THE PEANUT-BUTTER SAN'WICH WHICH HAS BEEN BLOCKIN' THE RECEPTION

S68

S69

Merrymole the magnificent

NOW IN PAPERBACK

An absorbing book for children, from about eight to twelve years, written and illustrated by Maurice Dodd.

The story recounts the hilarious adventures of an eccentric mole who wanted to live in the top of a tree. A story with excitement, pace, and full of incident – but above all, warmly humorous. Fully illustrated with lively and detailed drawings which perfectly complement the story; making a book which children will want to return to again and again.

Published in Piccolo £1.50.